M. J. GROVER

Agate Hunting on the Washington Coast

A Rockhounder's Guide to the Pacific Coast & Puget Sound

For more rockhounding adventures go to agatehunting.com

First edition

ISBN: 978-1-7362750-2-3

This book was professionally typeset on Reedsy.
Find out more at reedsy.com

Contents

Introduction

The beaches in this state are some of the most beautiful anywhere on Earth. There's nowhere quite like Western Washington. With miles of rocky shoreline and expansive vistas, the magic of this place should never be taken for granted.

Having done much of my rockhounding in Oregon, I quickly learned that things are a little different here in Washington. Whereas the entire coastline of Oregon is public land, the beaches of Washington are a patchwork of county, federal, private, state, and tribal lands. There is plenty of access, but there is also A LOT OF PRIVATE LAND and areas that are off-limits to most rockhounds.

Fortunately, there are also many, many points along the Pacific Coast, the Strait of Juan de Fuca, San Juan Islands and throughout Puget Sound that give you access to the shoreline. These are great beaches to explore and many of them will turn up some wonderful treasures! Agates, jaspers, sea glass, fossils, shells, sand dollars and other finds are just waiting to be discovered.

On my many rockhounding adventures in Washington over the years I found some beautiful agates, jaspers, and other treasures. I was hooked. I loved the hunt. **But many unproductive trips taught me that certain areas were much better than others. Not all beaches are equal for beachcombers and agate hunters.**

If you don't know where to go, there's a good chance you will go home empty-handed.

I started researching different areas and trying to figure out where to spend my time for the best results. There was certainly information out there, but it was scattered and vague. The rockhounding information that was available only mentioned a small selection of well-known areas that overlooked some of the better beaches.

I hope this guide book helps to fill that void. **There are literally thousands miles of coastline in Washington. There are many places to access the beach in Washington, and I have selected 33 of the very best beaches for agate hunting.** It's surely not all of them... and I have no doubt that there are still a few "secret" beaches out there for you to find. Use this as a guide and don't be afraid to explore some new spots too!

This list was compiled during several years of on-the-ground research and personal exploration. I have visited each of these sites several times, and every picture in this book was taken by me.

I hope this book helps you find some amazing agates.

Happy hunting!

Beautiful Treasures on the Beach

This book focuses primarily on agate hunting, but of course there are many other fun things to find when you are exploring Washington's beaches. Here is a quick overview of the different things you should keep an eye out for while you are visiting the beaches of Washington State.

Agates

Agate is a form of chalcedony that is usually semitransparent to translucent. If you find a rock on the beach that you can see through (even if it's foggy) then it's probably an agate. If a rock completely blocks light from passing through it, then it is not an agate.

Agates found on Washington beaches were formed in an area that had intense volcanic activity. This volcanic activity produced silica. Once the eruptions were over in a given place and the rain fell on the volcanic ashes, the silica in the ashes dissolved in the rainwater.

As the silica concentration in the water became high the water turned into a silica gel which was held in cavities or "vugs" in the lava and slowly crystallized into microcrystalline quartz. Erosion takes places and this material eventually finds its way into the ocean.

If the water-silica solution that crystallized to form the agate had impurities in it then various colors are the result, and these impurities are what make agates so beautiful.

Agates are often comprised of banded materials which can be identified by closely observing a specimen using a loupe or microscope. Hold the stone up to a flashlight and see if the light glows through it.

Select pieces that show nice banding are some of the most attractive agates that you can find. As you learn to find agates, you will soon realize that there are average agates, and then there are real "trophy" agates. No two pieces are exactly alike.

Most of the agates you can expect to find will range from the size of a jellybean on up to the size of a walnut. Put in enough time and you might get lucky and find one much larger than that. There are big ones out there!

Agates come in a wide array of colors, but certain colors will be more abundant depending on the area that you search. Along the beaches of the Pacific Ocean you will most commonly find agates ranging from clear to yellow or orange. There are even dark agates that are deep blue, purple and nearly black.

Jasper

For me, a nice jasper can be as big a treasure as an agate. Jaspers are structurally very similar to agates. They are both chalcedony, a microcrystalline quartz. However, while agates are transparent or translucent, jaspers are opaque. Light will not pass through them and they don't have the same "glassy" appearance that agates have.

Jaspers are still very beautiful though. They come in a wide variety of different colors. These variations in color will depend on the impurities within each stone. It is actually the impurities that give each piece of jasper its unique color. They can be found in yellows, greens, oranges, reds, purples, and other neat color variations.

Jaspers aren't necessarily just one solid color. They can often be a mottled mixture of many different colors within each stone. Orbicular jasper (also called "poppy" jasper) is of particular interest to Washington rockhounds. It is commonly found on the Pacific Coast and is a beautiful stone that is particularly nice for use in lapidary work.

You may also find a jasper that appears to have small pockets within the stone that appear to be more transparent. These are actually a mix of both jasper and agate, and are often referred to as "jasp-agates." Some of these aree very beautiful too, and will make a nice addition to your collection.

Fossils

Washington has got an amazing variety of fossils throughout the state, and the Pacific Coast and Puget Sound are certainly no exceptions. Most of the fossils that you might find on Washington beaches are marine invertebrates such as clams and snails. Many different species have been found and identified.

The sources of these fossils are ancient sea beds that have eroded over millions of years, releasing fossil specimens that are eventually washed up on the shore. There are ancient seashores that are now "high and dry" above the current water level. These cliffs contain many fossils that erode and are a continuous source of new fossils on the beaches.

Much less common are vertebrate fossils (teeth, bones, etc.). They are less common, but they are certainly out there. In fact, just as I am writing this, there was a recent story about a wooly mammoth tooth that was found by beachcombers on Camano Island. This certainly isn't the first time. In fact, there have been several mammoth teeth found on Camano Island, Whidbey

Island, and all throughout the Puget Sound. Mammoth fossils have been dug up at construction sites right in the heart of Seattle.

Petrified Wood

There are many different kinds of petrified wood to be found in Washington. Actually it is central and Eastern Washington that produce some of the best petrified wood specimens, but nice pieces also wash up on the beaches in Western Washington too.

Wood from various species can be found all along the Pacific Coast. Look for the telltale sign of growth rings and parallel lines to separate petrified wood from other beach stones. They can be harder to spot than your average beach stone, but they are out there.

Note: The Rice Northwest Museum of Rocks and Minerals in Hillsboro, Oregon has perhaps the most complete collection of Washington petrified wood specimens. Be sure to check it out if you are ever in the area. This is easily one of the best collection of minerals on display in the entire United States.

Driftwood

I'm sure it's no surprise that the Washington Coast has abundant driftwood. Pieces with fun, intricate shapes can be found just about anywhere, though hunting is always best after a good storm. They make great decorations around the home, and can be used for a variety of art projects.

Glass Fishing Floats

Fishing floats are one of the rarest and most treasured finds for Washington beachcombers. While they have been used by various cultures around the world, the ones that wash up on the Pacific coastline come from Asia. They are round glass balls that were used to float fishing nets.

These floats were produced by the hundreds of thousands in the early 1900s, primarily in Japan. They were made in a variety of colors and sizes. Of course, fishermen would lose their fishing gear from time to time, and the floats would be lost, making their way across the Pacific Ocean before eventually ending up somewhere along the coastline.

Throughout the 19th century, Japanese fishing floats were common along the Washington Coast. They are rare now, but occasionally show up even today. Major weather events that produce strong west winds bring them to shore.

Seashells

Washington isn't particularly well known for its seashells. While we certainly don't have the abundance or variety of shells that warmer climates have, you can still find some nice shells from time to time. The difference is that most PNW shells are fairly drab in color, not the flashy shells that you might expect to find in Hawaii or Florida.

Perhaps the most common prize on the Washington Coast is the sand dollar. They are flat and white with a "star" on the top. These are fairly common is certain areas under the right conditions. They are usually broken, but you can find them intact if you look hard enough.

Sea Glass

Sea glass is simply a shard of broken glass that has spent years tumbling in the ocean. The result is a tiny, frosty "pebble" of glass. Clear, green and brown are going to be the most common, but you can get lucky and find blues, reds and purples. The best beaches for sea glass hunting are close to old dump sights.

Back in the old days, it was quite common for towns to dump their garbage into the ocean. Obviously this was a problem for a variety of ecological reasons, but it did put a lot of glass into the ocean. As a result there is sea glass constantly being washed up on the beaches.

Of course, modern glass also finds its way into the ocean from time to time. I don't get too excited about sea glass if I can still make out the curved shape of a glass shard, but a fully tumbled piece of glass into a smooth round "stone" is definitely a cool find. For some, these beautiful water worn frosty pieces of glass are the ultimate beach treasure.

Gold & Platinum

Most people are quite surprised to hear that they can find gold at the Washington Coast. Actually, there was a short-lived gold rush to the beaches of Washington during the 1860s, and mining continued on and off for many years.

The gold is found as tiny particles within the beach sands. You can use a standard gold pan to carefully separate those tiny flakes of gold from lighter sand.

The richest beach in the state is at Cape Disappointment at the mouth of the Columbia River. You may need to do a bit of "prospecting," but the best spots are generally easy to find because you will see black sands. These are sands that contain iron, and are heavier than the lighter colored sands. These black sands are where you will find the gold.

Small historic gold and platinum mining efforts have taken place in Clallam County, at Shi Shi Beach, Ruby Beach, Moclips, the old Starbuck Mine south of Ozette Lake, near the mouth of Ozette River and many other sites along the Pacific Coast. Some of these areas are now within the Olympic National Park and would be best to avoid, but there are plenty of other sites that can be explored.

Don't expect to get rich, but it's pretty fun to do, and yet another treasure that you can find on Washington beaches. Make sure you check the latest rules about the types of equipment that you are allowed to use depending on your location.

"Tumbler Material"

This is a term that I will use from time to time to describe a wide array of different rock types that are hard enough to take a nice polish if you put them in a rock tumbler.

All that is really required for a rock to take a nice polish is to be dense enough that the grit will polish the surface of the rock. You'll find smooth quartz rocks that I call "sugar agates" which resemble agates when they are wet, but have a frosty look when they are wet. These, and most any agate, chalcedony, jasper, quartz, and petrified wood will take a good polish.

Part of the fun of using a rock tumbler is to put stones in it and just see how they turn out. Sometimes what you put in won't polish up, but sometimes you will be blown away with what comes out of the tumbler. Rock tumbling is a fun hobby that goes hand in hand with rockhounding.

10 Tips for More Successful Agate Hunting

Agates are highly sought after prizes throughout the world. We are lucky here in the Pacific Northwest to have so many places to search for them. Here are some tips and tricks that will help you find these beautiful treasures!

1. Hit the Gravel Areas of Beaches and Rivers

No matter whether you are hunting along a beach or a river, you will have the best luck if you seek out gravel areas. Long, sandy beaches with little or no cobble material generally aren't very productive. Look for areas where the waves have exposed rocky shores or tossed up material on top of the sand. When river hunting for agates, search when the water is low and gravel bars are exposed.

2. Sunny Days

Sun can be a rare commodity during the winters in Washington. When it does show itself, I like to get out and find some agates! By walking the beaches on a sunny day you will notice that those lovely translucent agates really "glow" and are much easier to spot.

3. After Storms or Large Waves

Any time there are big storms and large waves along the coast, you can bet that there will be some nice agates that get washed ashore. The ocean is constantly replenishing the beaches with new material. If the forecast calls for a big storm, followed by a clear sunny day, you'd better get out there! Beachcombing should be excellent.

4. Hunt Low Tide

Being out there when tides are going down is prime time for beachcombing. Waves leave treasures "high and dry" and they are just waiting for you to come and pick them up. Similarly, if you are hunting along creeks and rivers, go out during the summertime when water levels are low and gravel bars are exposed.

5. Be Patient

Agates are relatively common if you are in a good area, but it still takes some patience to find them. If you only spend 20 minutes looking, or you don't walk very far from a popular parking area, then you probably aren't going to have much luck. Put on some good rain gear and hiking boots and plan to spend a few hours out there.

6. Hit the Good Locations

Some places are definitely better than others when it comes to agate hunting. As mentioned before, the gravel beaches are usually best, but that isn't the only thing that makes a beach good for agate hunting. Do your research and spend your time in the most productive spots.

7. Sift Through Gravels

Some of the better spots have lots of heavy gravel deposits. Beachcombers will come along and pick up the obvious agates on the surface, but there are lots more that are hidden right beneath the surface. Simply sit down and dig through gravels to expose the treasures beneath. In loose gravels you can simply use your hands or a small beach trowel.

8. Learn to Identify Agates, Jaspers, and Petrified Wood

Identification is very important because there are a lot of interesting things on the beach that aren't necessarily easy to spot. You probably won't have much trouble seeing those brilliant yellow or orange carnelian agates, but what about the duller colored red jaspers or fragments of petrified wood? Even some of the nicest agates don't look very exciting until you get them home and put them through a rock tumbler.

9. Use a Treasure Scoop

It can be tiring to bend down hundreds of times to inspect little fragments among the gravels. A simple little treasure scoop can really save your back, especially if you are getting up there in years.

10. Get out before the Crowds

This is a big one. Do your best to get to your favorite agate hunting spot first at prime time. This means you should be on the beach just prior to low tide. Early mornings are also great because the waves have had all night to expose new agates.

Regulations: Rockhounding on Washington Beaches

The purpose of this book is to tell you where agates can be found, but **ultimately it is your responsibility to research the laws and regulations for the sites where you are collecting rocks. This book tells you where to find agates... whether or not you decide to pick them up and put them in your pocket is your decision.** Do your due diligence and make your choices regarding where you want to collect.

While doing research for this section, I found it somewhat fascinating that most of the folks working for the agencies that manage the various access sites in this book did not know the rules either. This is what I could find...

Most county parks throughout Western Washington do not make any mention of rockhounding in any of their regulations. As far as I can tell, collecting rocks at county parks throughout Western Washington is just fine.

I also couldn't find much information on tribal lands, but the general consensus I have gotten from talking to folks is that it simply isn't an issue. As long as you are respectful and follow the general posted rules of the reservation, collecting a few rocks is no problem.

Many of the best accesses to Washington beaches are at state parks. I sent a few different emails to Washington State Parks and was told that casually picking up rocks is just fine as long as you don't do any digging. A discussion with a park ranger at one of the State Parks in Puget Sound told me I was fine picking up agates, just avoid digging in the bluffs. Aside from that he had no issues. I've talked to a few rockhounds that have been picking up agates at state parks for decades and never had any troubles at all.

The only area where I could find any clear information that officially said rockhounding was off-limits was within the Olympic National Park. The official law regarding mineral collection within National Parks reads:

"Collecting, rockhounding, and gold panning of rocks, minerals, and paleontological specimens, for either recreational or educational purposes is generally prohibited in all units of the National Park System (36 C.F.R. § 2.1(a) and § 2.5(a)). Violators of this prohibition are subject to criminal penalties."

This law is pretty clear, yet I spoke with a ranger about beachcombing once when I was at Ruby Beach and was told, and I quote, "We're really not too concerned with that." Just keep in mind that he was specifically talking about picking up a few rocks off the beach. I can certainly understand that a National Park is not the place for digging and mining, which is why that law is in place. Casually picking up some rocks along the shoreline seems to be of little concern, at least to the ranger that I was talking with. I can't guarantee the one you run into will be as friendly though...

Overall, my "gut feeling" (which has been confirmed by many of the Washington rockhounds that I have spoken to) is that picking up rocks simply isn't a concern for most of the management agencies.

Be respectful, make sure you've got the appropriate parking/access permits, don't dig a bunch of holes or bring buckets, and avoid the bluffs and other unstable areas. Collecting a few rocks should be no problem.

Finding the Sites in this Book

Each site in this book has a short section with driving directions to the beach. I was a bit torn on just how much detail to add in this section. Filling up pages with super specific driving directions to each site seems a bit redundant in an era when just about everyone has a smartphone and can easily plug in the site information and find where they are going. Most of these sites are state and county parks, so they won't be too hard to find. Yet it wouldn't be much of a guide book if I didn't actually tell you how to get there, would it?

Here are a few thoughts:

First, I realize that not everyone will be coming from the same direction. Therefore, I generally make the starting point the nearest decent sized town. This varies a bit from site to site, but I assume that the reader can at least get close. Navigate to the closest town, then from there follow my directions to access the beach.

Second, although it's not too common these days, I realize there are still a few folks who don't carry a cell phone, or they still use a good old-fashioned flip phone. I want this book to be useful for you as well.

Third, there are a handful of sites, notably those along the Strait of Juan de Fuca and sections of the Pacific Coast, where cell phone coverage is spotty. Obviously, you will want to be able to find the sites even when your cell phone doesn't work.

Spend a few extra minutes to plan out your visit to the beach before you leave home, so that you have a general idea of where you will be going that day. Pull up Google Maps and check out the location of the sites. I always keep a copy of the **Washington Delorme Atlas & Gazetteer** in my pickup, and I would encourage you to do the same.

It's also wise to let friends and family know where you are going, particularly if you are visiting some of the more secluded areas.

Staying Safe on your Rockhounding Adventures

I don't want to exaggerate the risks associated with agate hunting, but it is worth mentioning them so that we all have a safe trip while exploring Washington's beaches. Agates certainly aren't so important that we should risk our health and safety.

Of course millions of people explore the shores of Puget Sound and the Pacific Coast in Washington every year without incident. Unfortunately, every year a few people perish in various avoidable situations. So let's take a quick look at some dangers so we can make sure that we are reasonably prepared.

Weather

Everyone knows that rain is a part of life in this part of the world. Be prepared to get wet. Even on a warm, sunny day, rain clouds can blow in quickly over the Pacific and change the weather drastically. Winters here are generally predictable... wet and cold.

Be prepared with the proper gear and clothing before you head out. Dress in several layers and always have some good rain gear with you, so you are ready for whatever comes. Wear a good pair of boots during the the winter months and keep them oiled up!

Storms & Waves

Agate hunting and winter storms go hand in hand as far as I am concerned. Those nasty storms that blow over the Pacific Ocean and pummel the Pacific Northwest with wind and rain also strip sand off the beaches and expose agates and jaspers. Serious agate hunters love a good storm.

However, these storms create large waves that must be respected. Never turn your back on the mighty Pacific Ocean. Large waves can come at you unexpectedly and ruin a good day. You may think this sounds like an exaggeration, but people die every year on the Washington Coast because of these "sneaker waves."

This may be less of a concern if you are on a long sandy beach, but often we agate hunters find ourselves scrambling around in rocks, exploring low tide pools, and crawling through driftwood and other structures. Large waves can easily cause people to lose their footing, slip down among large rocks, or get trapped under driftwood. Huge pieces of driftwood can be moved by just a few inches of fast moving water, so never stand or sit on driftwood near the waves.

Wild Animals

Wildlife is one of the things that makes the beaches so fun to visit. While most of them aren't all that dangerous, we still need to be respectful of the critters out here.

Seals and sea lions are common throughout Washington. You need to keep your distance from them. During calving season in particular it is imperative that you keep your distance. Make sure your kids are aware, and keep dogs leashed during this time of the year. Not only is it the safe thing to do, but it's also illegal to harass wildlife.

There are bears and mountain lions all throughout Washington. You aren't very likely to encounter them if you are walking on the beach, but you might if you explore some of the creeks and rivers that drain into the Pacific Ocean. The best advice if you encounter a bear or mountain lion is to give them their space, and slowly back away. Actual attacks on humans are exceedingly rare and nothing to be overly concerned about, in my opinion.

Plants & Bugs

A more real concern is bugs! There are all kinds of flying, stinging, and biting critters that you might encounter. Ticks are not uncommon during the spring and summer. Definitely bring some insect repellent with you, particularly during the warmer months.

There are a few plants to avoid. Most noteworthy is Poison Oak, which can really ruin your day if you get into it. You'll probably be fine if you are simply beachcombing, but it does grow in the mountains nearby. Blackberries and other thorny plants are also abundant.

Cliffy Areas

Use caution when exploring around rocky areas and along cliff walls. The ocean waves erode and undercut them and can cause sand, dirt and rocks to fall on your head. Rocks can be slippery and a large wave can easily knock a person down if you are standing on one. Many bluffs are comprised of loose aggregated gravel that can easily collapse and fall on you if you are too close. Use caution.

Break-ins

Unfortunately, break-ins seem to be getting more and more common these days. This is definitely a problem at some of the parking areas where you have to hike away from your car to access the more remote beaches. Be sure to lock your doors and avoid leaving any valuables visible in your car. Clean out your glove box and leave it wide open. Some people even prefer to leave their doors unlocked, so at least their window won't get broken if someone does decide to rifle through it.

Supplies & Services

Keep in mind that some of the sites in this book are a good distance from large towns. It's a good idea to load up on food and supplies before you leave home, or at least make sure that stores you plan to use are open. A lot of small business in the more remote parts of Washington, particularly in the winter, will be closed at unexpected times. Don't always assume that stores will be open.

Exploring the Beach

Don't let any of this scare you away from visiting the beach. Every year millions of people have a safe and fun trip that goes by without incident, so there is no need to be fearful. I simply want people to be prepared, just as with any outdoor adventure that you might have.

All in all, searching for agates is a safe and fun activity suitable for anyone. Just be smart and use the appropriate level of caution just as you would for any outdoor activity. And don't forget the rain gear!

North Puget Sound (Site Map)

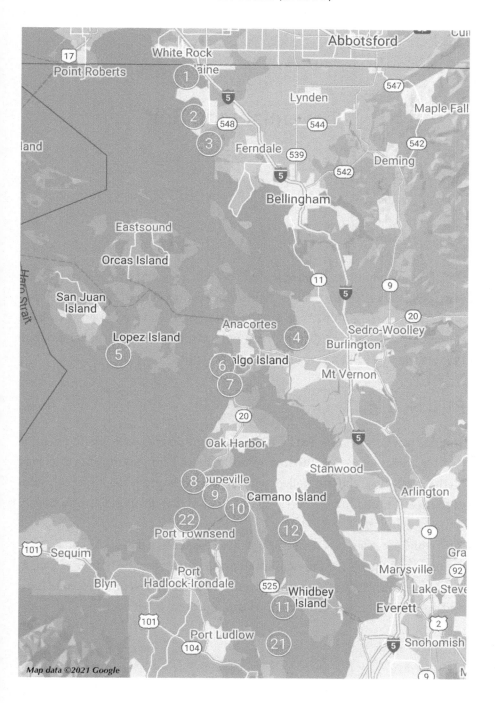

1. Semiahmoo Spit

Directions:

Heading north on I-84 toward the B.C. border, take exit 270 and go west on Birch Bay Lynden Rd. for 4 miles. At the intersection, turn right on Harborview Rd. Continue straight until you get to the harbor, then veer left onto Drayton Harbor Rd. for another 2.5 miles. Turn right at the intersection of Semiahmoo Parkway and you will arrive at the site in 0.5 miles.

Field Notes:

This is a free access managed by Whatcom County Parks & Recreation. A large parking area is located on the south side, and a smaller parking area is located on the north side. You can walk down and search the gravel beds on both sides of the spit. I found more interesting material on the Strait of Georgia side.

The public access is over a mile of beach access (both sides of the spit). There are outstanding views of the mountains and city across the border in British Columbia. The Alaska Packers Association Cannery Museum is located here, and open to tour from Memorial Day through September.

Semiahmoo Spit. Stunning views looking north into British Columbia!

2. Birch Bay State Park

Directions:

Heading north on I-84 toward the B.C. border, take exit 270 and go west on Birch Bay Lynden Rd. for 4 miles. Take a left at the intersection onto Birch Bay Dr., and continue south through Birch Bay for about 2 miles. The park is on the south end of town.

Field Notes:

Discover Pass required. Birch Bay State Park provides approximately 1 mile of beach access within the park. There are also a few smaller access points to the beach in the town of Birch Bay that are outside of the park.

The beaches of Whatcom County are known to turn up some nice agates and this one is no exception. I found a few small agates and some decent beach glass on my last visit. The park also has nice facilities for picnicking and hiking.

There are lots of camping sites which can be reserved online. Clamming in the bay is productive in Birch Bay and a popular activity when the season is on.

2. BIRCH BAY STATE PARK

3. Cherry Point

Directions:

From downtown Ferndale, go east on Main St. (it quickly turns into Mountain View Rd.) for approximately 4.8 miles. Turn right on Rainbow Rd. and continue for 1 mile, then turn left on Henry Rd. Drive for about 1.3 miles and you will come to a gate, and make a left turn on Gulf Rd. Continue a few hundred yards and you will arrive at Cherry Point Beach.

Field Notes:

This is a great site for those of you who are looking to get away from the crowds. Cherry Point is a day-use access. Note that the beach is public, but the adjacent lands are not. Judging from all the "No Trespassing, No Beach Fires, Day-Use Only" signs you'll see on the drive in, it's safe to say that you should stick close to the shoreline.

This is a great rocky shoreline to explore. There is a derelict conveyor at the parking area. From there, you can walk either direction and rockhound to your heart's desire. There is a good chance of finding agates and jaspers at this site, and without the crowds that you will find at nearby Birch Bay.

Abandoned conveyor at Cherry Point.

4. Bay View State Park

Directions:

Take exit 231 just north of Burlington. Drive west for about 6.5 miles, all the way to Bayview. Turn north on Bayview Edison Rd. and look for the park in about 0.3 miles.

Field Notes:

Discover Pass required. Due to its smaller size and limited access to shoreline I almost didn't include this site in the book. However, I found a big beautiful clear/white agate in the first 20 seconds that I started hunting here, so I took that as a sign that I needed to include it. Lots of big, white quartz here too.

There is only a few hundred yards of gravelly shoreline to explore here so it won't take you too long, but it's still a decent site to check out. There will be a lot less people here than at many other sites which is always a plus, but it could easily get picked over if another agate hunter gets here before you do.

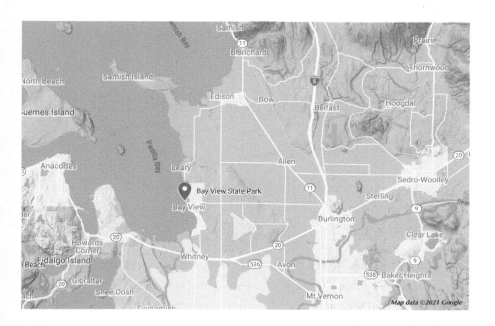

This big 3" clear/white agate greeted me at Bayview State Park.

5. San Juan Island National Historic Park

Directions:

You'll have to take the ferry to San Juan Island to access this site. Online reservations are recommended to prevent long wait times. From Anacortes, take Highway 20 for about 3.5 miles to the ferry site. Toll fee required. Take the ferry to Friday Harbor. As you drive off the ferry, continue southwest on Spring Street for about 0.5 miles. Turn left on Mullis Road (turns into Cattle Point Road) and continue south for 8 miles. Follow signs to the beach.

Field Notes:

This site is managed by the National Park Service. No fee to access the beach. You can take the fascinating tour of Fort Flagler for a nominal fee. This park has many miles of rocky shoreline to explore, more than any other in Washington. You can explore the north shore at Fourth of July Beach and Jakles Lagoon. On the south shore check out Grandma's Cove, South Beach and Cattle Point. You can't go wrong here... there are good gravel beds everywhere and you are likely to find agates just about anywhere.

This is one of my favorite sites in this book. It takes a little extra effort to get out here, but it's worth it. There aren't any camp sites within the park, but there are plenty of options available on the island. It might be worthwhile to plan to stay a few days on the island to get the most out of this location.

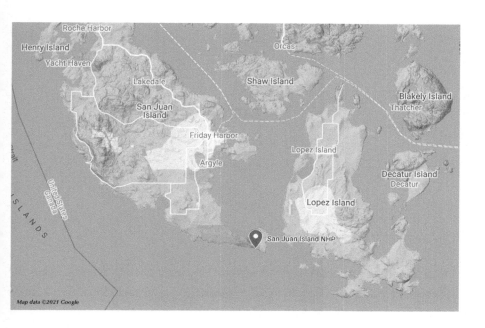

Lots of colorful gravel to explore on San Juan Island.

6. Rosario Beach

Directions:

From downtown Anacortes, head west on Highway 20 to D Avenue. Continue this route (changes to Havekost Rd. > Marine Dr. > Rosario Rd.) for 7.7 miles to Cougar Gap Rd. Turn on Rosario Beach Rd. at the entrance and follow it down to the parking area.

Field Notes:

Discover Pass required. This is a very fun beach to explore with a lot of variety, and it's a great site to bring the kids. You will easily find a wide assortment of beach rocks of different colors, and plenty of "sugar agates" that glow beautifully when they are wet. There are two easily accessible beaches on each side of Rosario Head. Both are worth checking out. Probably somewhere between 0.25 and 0.5 miles of gravel shoreline to explore here.

While you are here, you could also check out nearby Bowman Bay. You can take a 0.5 mile hike to get there along the shore, or you can drive back out and turn west on Rosario Road. Go for about a mile and look for the entrance. I didn't find as many interesting rocks here, but it's a larger beach and is still worth exploring if you have the time.

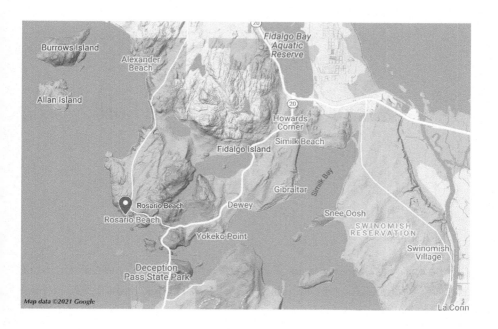

Fun variety of colorful rocks found at Rosario Beach.

7. Deception Pass State Park

Directions:

From downtown Anacortes, head west on Highway 20 to D Avenue. Continue this route (changes to Havekost Rd. > Marine Dr. > Rosario Rd.) for about 9 miles. Turn right, crossing over Deception Pass Bridge and continue for about 2 miles to the entrance of Deception Pass State Park.

Field Notes:

Discover Pass required. This is Washington's most visited state park, and it is quite exceptional. Make sure you stop at the overlook by the bridge before you drop down. You will be greeted with miles of shoreline to explore on both North Beach and West Beach. There are big cobbles here and millions of rocks to search through. You'll find some agates here if you put in enough time. Nice jaspers and other nice tumbler materials are usually pretty easy to find.

Please note that Deception Pass can be quite dangerous with extremely high flows (over 50 times the average flow volume of all the rivers that drain into Puget Sound). Suffice it to say that extra caution should be taken at this site and keep an extra close eye on children here.

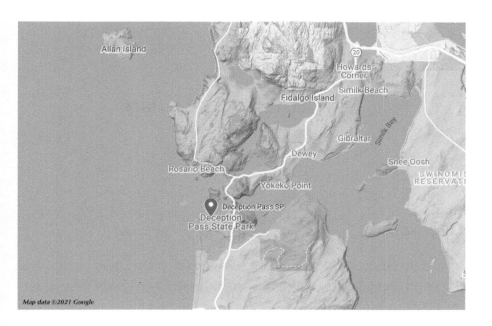

One of the most beautiful places in Puget Sound.

8. Fort Ebey State Park

Directions:

From Oak Harbor, continue down Highway 20 toward the southern tip of the island. In about 6.5 miles, turn west on Libbey Rd. and continue for about 1 mile. Take a left turn on Hill Valley Dr. and follow it to the entrance of the park. Follow the signs to access the beach.

Field Notes:

Discover Pass required. Fort Ebey was constructed as a coastal defense fort during World War II. Now it is a state park with fascinating history and extensive rocky beaches to explore. Whidbey Island is a well-known location for agate hunters, but unfortunately the vast majority of the shoreline is privately owned and not open to the public. Fort Ebey is one of only a handful of places where the public can scour the beaches for rocks.

Lots of fun and interesting rocks cover the shoreline. You will notice in some areas that there are towering bluffs of loosely aggregated gravel. Be extra careful, as these cliffs are unstable and rocks are eroding from them continuously. Excellent tumbler material can be found here and with a little time and luck you should have no trouble finding a few agates at this site as well.

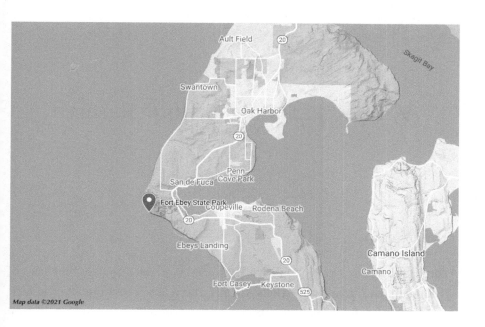

3 nice agates found on the beach at Fort Ebey State Park.

9. Ebey's Landing Historic Reserve

Directions:

From Oak Harbor, continue down Highway 20 toward the southern tip of Whidbey Island. In about 9 miles, turn right on S. Sherman Rd. At the fork, angle to the left onto Cook Rd., then turn right onto Ebey's Landing Rd. You can park in the small parking lot just as you reach the beach, or continue onto Hill Rd. for overflow parking on the side of the road before it climbs the grade.

Field Notes:

Discover Pass required. This is another great stretch of rocky shoreline along Whidbey Island's east shore where a diligent beachcomber can recover some very nice agates. If you are up for a hike, there is a great trail here that lets you do a 5.6 mile loop, climbing the bluffs and looping around Perego's Lagoon, then dropping down to the beach for the loop back. Wonderful views of the Olympic Mountains.

There are several miles of beach access with nice gravel as far as you can see. This site (and nearby Fort Ebey State Park) provide the most access of anywhere on Whidbey Island, and the agate hunting is very good here. This is a very popular site, but still plenty of rocks to go around!

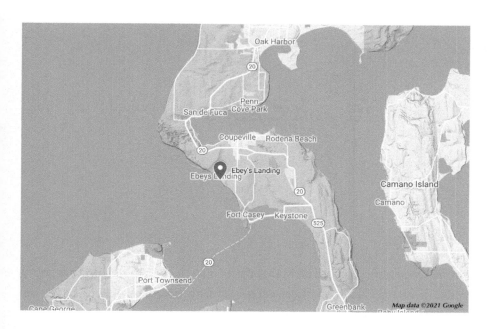

A very popular spot to find agates. Several miles of prime pickin' at this site.

10. Fort Casey State Park

Directions:

From Coupeville, go south on Main Street (turns into S. Engle Rd.) for about 4 miles to arrive at Fort Casey Beach. There is a large parking lot here, or you can continue east toward Keystone and you will see several more parking spots along the spit. At the farthest end is an access at Driftwood Park.

Field Notes:

Discover Pass required. This is another good access on the east side of Whidbey Island. This is where the ferry leaves for Port Townsend. With the different access points along the spit, you've got about 1 mile of shoreline to explore here. On the far east side toward Keystone is Driftwood Park, a smaller park managed by Island County. If you don't want to worry about a recreation pass, you could park here for free and still have access to some rocky shoreline for agate hunting.

I had a stare down with a bald eagle at this site. Of course there are lots of other interesting birds to look at here, just as there are all over Puget Sound, but nearby Crockett Lake also attracts a lot.

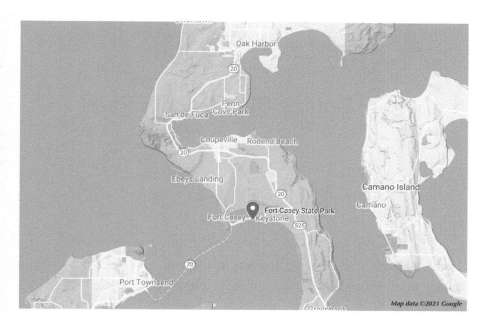

A pretty little agate perched atop the gravel.

11. Double Bluff County Park

Directions:

From Freeland, head west on Highway 525 for about 1 mile. Turn right on Double Bluff Rd. and head south. In about 2 miles you will arrive at Double Bluff County Park.

Field Notes:

This is a park maintained by Island County. There is no fee at this site, but parking is somewhat limited and may be an issue in the busy season. This is also an off-leash area so it's popular with dog owners. Consider getting here early to find a parking spot. There is more sand here than at most other accesses on Whidbey Island, but there's still enough gravel here to keep you interested.

The parking area is adjacent to private beaches, but you can walk the opposite direction toward the bluffs and you will find plenty of gravel beds to explore. Be wary of the bluffs as they are unstable and dangerous, but the beach below is fine as long as you stay far enough away. Lots of seashells at this site too.

Scattered gravels. Better material toward the bluffs, but be careful.

12. Camano Island State Park

Directions:

From Camano, head south on West Camano Dr. for 2.5 miles. Turn right on Lowell Point Rd. and head into the park. Wind your way through and follow the signs to the beach, about 2 more miles.

Field Notes:

Discover Pass required. Camano Island has an unfortunate lack of access. Despite having over 50 miles of shoreline, there are only a small handful of areas where the general public can access the beach. One access to a few miles of shoreline is at Camano Island State Park. It's a great locations for rockhounds, and there are a few places to check out. You can park down at the boat ramp and explore the rocky shorelines in either direction. I visited on a nasty rainy day and headed south around Lowell Point. It was cold and miserable, but I found a half dozen nice agates.

Backtrack up West Camano Dr. and you can explore more beaches at Cama Beach Historical State Park. There is camping, miles of trails, boat rentals and cabin rentals. This is a beautiful place to spend some time. Visit in the off-season and it won't be so busy, plus the agate hunting is usually better.

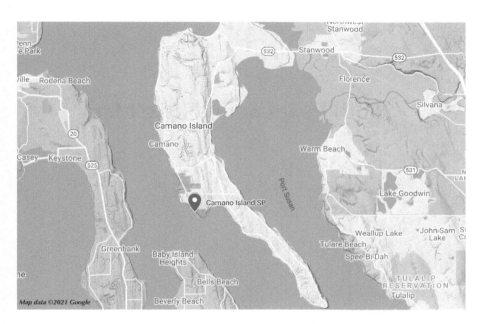

A bunch of nice agates from Camano Island. Neat variety!

South Puget Sound (Site Map)

13. Sequalitchew Creek Trail

Directions:

Take Exit 118 from I-5, and turn west toward Dupont. Continue through town on Center Drive for about 1.5 miles. Turn left on Civic Drive (there is a sign for Sequalitchew Creek Trailhead) and the parking area for the trailhead is on your right, next to City Hall.

Field Notes:

Plenty of parking and no fee to park. Interesting history here. This is the site of Fort Nisqually, built by the Hudson Fur Company back in the 1830s. A century later the Dupont Company built an explosives factory here. Now the land is owned by the city of Dupont and provides access for the public to explore.

This is a lovely 1.5 mile trail that follows along Sequalitchew Creek. At the end of the trail you will walk through a tunnel underneath the train tracks and pop out on the beach. This is a popular trail for hikers, but you'll find less people here than the beaches closer to Seattle with easier access. The hike is easy, but the 3 mile round-trip does help to limit the traffic. Not much luck searching amongst the bigger rocks, but up higher on the beach were the smaller "pea gravels" that had some treasures hidden in them. Found several nice small agates ranging from clear to yellow/orange, and lots of jaspers and other good little stones to bring back for the tumbler.

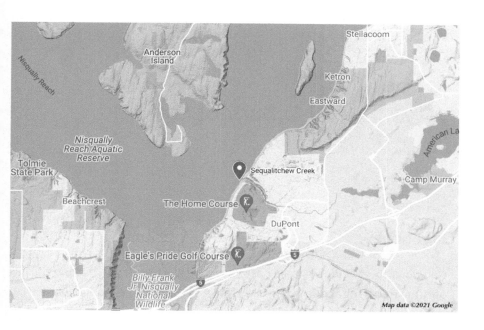

It's a bit of a hike, but well worth it!

14. Burfoot Park

Directions:

From downtown Olympia, take East Bay Drive Northeast north along the bay. Continue north for about 7 miles and look for the entrance to Burfoot Park.

Field Notes:

This is a Thurston County Park with no parking fee. Nice facilities including bathrooms and playground. Access to the beach requires a fairly short, moderate hike (<0.25 mile) down to the water's edge.

There is a fairly short stretch of beach access here, probably a few hundred yards at most. Certainly not the largest beach access in this book, but it's a nice option for folks in the Olympia area, and slightly less popular compared to nearby Priest Point Park (which requires a Discover Pass). Nice solid gravel beds and lots of smaller rocks that will give you plenty to search through.

Be cautious. There are signs on the trail warning about poison ivy. I can tell you from personal experience, it's no fun!

Clear agate found at the beach at Burfoot Park. Watch out for poison ivy!

15. Harstine Island State Park

Directions:

From Shelton, head east on Highway 3 for about 8 miles. Turn right on East Pickering Drive and continue for 4.5 miles to the East Pickering Bridge. Immediately after the bridge, turn left on East North Island Drive and continue for 3.5 miles. Turn right on East Harstine Island Road N for about a mile. Look for the entrance to the park and continue to the parking area.

Field Notes:

Discover Pass required. Parking area is small, suitable for about 10 vehicles, although this is a less popular park than many others so parking shouldn't be an issue most of the time. You still may want to arrive early at peak times of the year. Bathrooms are available at the parking area, but its a bit of a hike down to the beach so keep that in mind.

It's a decent little 1/4 mile hike down to the beach with a moderately steep descent. It's a good trail, but this site might not be for everyone. I'm in good shape, but it will definitely get your heart pumping on the hike out. The hike is absolutely beautiful though, and this park is harder to get to than many others so you'll probably run into fewer people here. I've found a nice abundance of red jaspers at this site, with the occassional agate to keep things exciting.

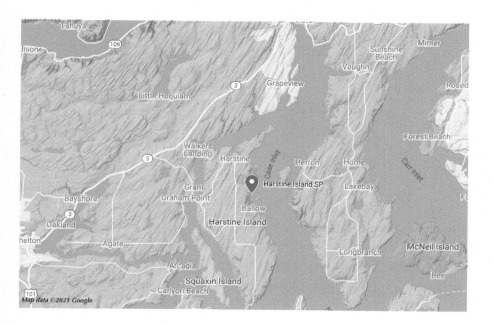

It's a nice hike to the beach, but you'll definitely work up a sweat hiking back out.

16. Joemma Beach State Park

Directions:

Penrose Point State Park is located on the Key Peninsula. Whichever direction you are coming from, you will need to take the Exit south from Highway 302 and head south on the Key Peninsula Highway NW toward the town of Home. From Home, continue south for 1.3 miles. Turn right on Whiteman Road SW and continue south for another 1.3 miles. Turn right on Bay Road SW and follow the signs to the parking area.

Field Notes:

Discover Pass required. Bathrooms available. There is a fishing pier and boat launch at this site as well. This is an easy access with beach access close to the parking lot. Far enough from the major cities that it's usually nice and quiet here compared to some of the other more popular state parks.

There is about 3000' of beach access. Pay attention to the signage marking the boundary to be sure that you aren't trespassing on adjacent private property.

My last visit to this site was at low tide and I found some nice amber colored agates, several nice "sugar agates" and a few jaspers. Not too bad for a warm spring day...

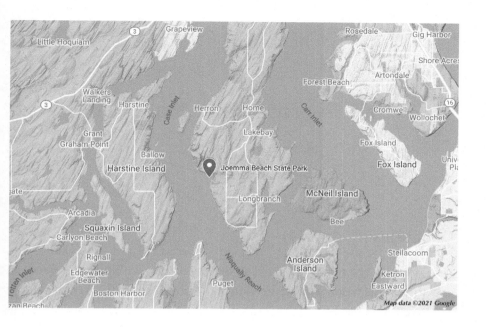

Pretty rocks on a warm spring day. Nothing better!

17. Penrose Point State Park

Directions:

Penrose Point State Park is located on the Key Peninsula. Whichever direction you are coming from, you will need to take the Exit south from Highway 302 and head south on the Key Peninsula Highway NW toward the town of Home. From Home, continue south for another mile, then turn left on Cornwall Road SW. Turn right on Delano SW, then right again on 158th Avenue SW to arrive at Penrose Point State Park.

Field Notes:

Discover Pass required. Bathrooms available at parking lot. There is easy access at the main parking area, but the beach adjacent to the parking lot is adjacent to Mayo Cove and not necessarily the best place to search since the beach is more silty here. The best rockhounding will be found if you take the trails that access the beaches on the east side of the park and up toward Penrose Point (the actual point of land). This is a productive area with plenty of agates. There are over 2 miles of shoreline to explore, with the majority of it being nice and rocky.

The area closer to the parking area is still a neat spot to explore and a great place to bring the kids. Although the rockhounding is poor closer to the parking lot, I did find lots of interesting shells and sand dollars.

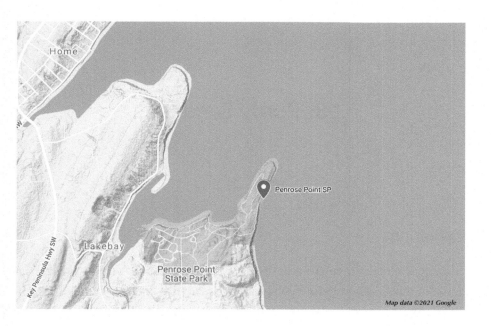

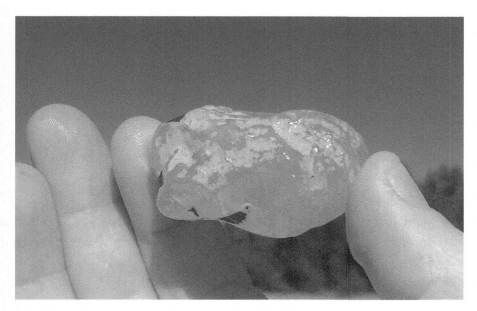

Take the trails and search the east shoreline for the best agate hunting.

18. Purdy Sand Spit

Directions:

From Tacoma, head northwest of Highway 16 for about 12 miles toward the town of Purdy. Right before you get into town, turn and cross the Purdy Bay Bridge that crosses over Henderson Bay. The highway follows right along the spit. There is no parking lot, but you can pull alongside at wide spots along the highway. I drove past the beach, then turned around so I was approaching from the west since there were wider turnoffs on the south side of the road.

Field Notes:

This wouldn't be my top destination, primarily because the highway runs right along the beach. The road noise doesn't make for the most relaxing beach experience, but it's a decent spot to do some beachcombing so its certainly worth visiting if you are in the area.

I've found more oyster and clam shells on this beach than agates, but you'll certainly find a few if you put in the time. I found a few nice jaspers and a rough clear/smoky agate on my last visit to Purdy. Not a huge variety of color in the beach rocks, but a few jaspers scattered across the beach.

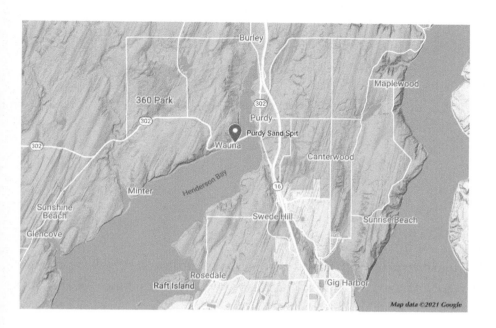

Best to approach this site from west to east. No parking lot. Find a wide spot along the road.

19. Kopachuck State Park

Directions:

From downtown Gig Harbor, head west on Rosedale Street NW for approximately 3 miles. Turn left on Ray Nash Drive NW and continue for about 0.7 miles. Continue straight (the road name changes to Kopachuck Drive NW) for about 1.5 miles. Turn right on 56th Street and follow the signs to Kopachuck State Park.

Field Notes:

Discover Pass required. Bathroom is available up top at the parking area. There is a decent amount of parking, but this is a popular site that can fill up on weekends. Consider getting here early in the day. There is a modest hike (a few hundred yards) down to the beach.

This park provides about 1 mile of rocky shoreline to explore, with great views of the Olympic Mountains and Cutts Island. I never seem to find any agates here, but I'm sure there are a few around. There are always plenty of jaspers and other hard rocks that would take a nice polish in a rock tumbler.

If you're looking for an adventure, you could launch kayaks from here and paddle over to Cutts Island State Park which is only about 0.5 miles off shore.

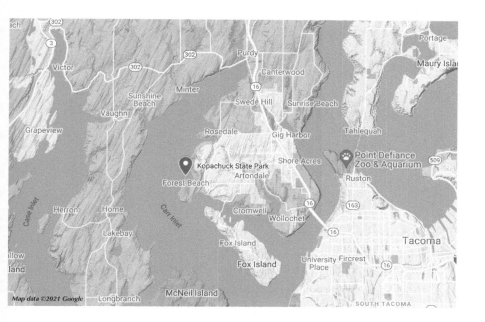

Standing at Kopachuck State Park looking across to Cutts Island.

20. Anderson Point County Park

Directions:

From Olalla, go north on Banner Road for about 0.5 miles. Turn on Millihanna and go 0.25 miles to reach the parking area. This is a Kitsap County Park with no fee. The parking area is situated well above the water, and you'll have to hike down a moderate grade to get to the beach.

Field Notes:

The hike from the parking lot to the beach is about 0.5 miles. Personally I always like a short hike because it means less people, but you'll want to keep that in mind as it may be too much for some people. It's definitely a good workout hiking back up to the parking lot at the end of the day.

Even though there isn't all that much beach access at this site, I have done well here. In fact on both of my visits to this site I had the beach all to myself. There is about 0.25 miles of shoreline to explore, as the private land on each side of the park is well posted and off-limits. The rocks are plentiful and there are agates to find if you look close.

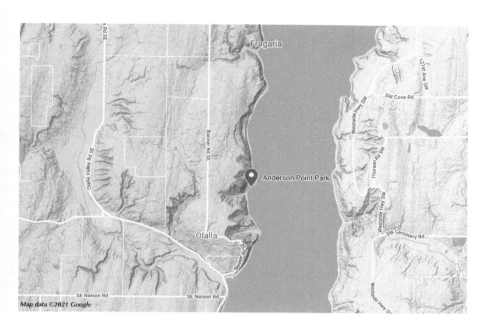

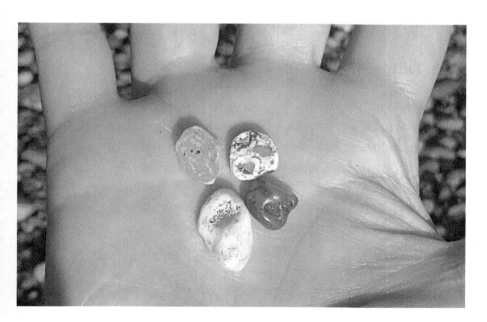

21. Point No Point County Park

Directions:

Point No Point is situated at the northeast point of the Kitsap Peninsula. It is a fair distance from any of the larger towns, but the nearest one to navigate to is Hansville. From Hansville, you will head east on Twin Spits Rd. for 0.5 miles. Turn east on Point No Point Road and drive for about a mile until you reach the parking lot at the lighthouse.

Field Notes:

This is a Kitsap County Park, so there is no parking fee. Drive past the boat ramp to the main parking area. Often the northfacing beach is very sandy and won't be productive for agates. It's generally best to walk around the point, past the lighthouse and down the beach on the east side.

This isn't a cobbly beach of solid rocks, but there are plenty of rocks to search through nonetheless. There is over a 0.5 miles of beach access and plenty of area to explore.

There is a variety of material here, and you can find some decent beach glass on occasion. If you are up for it, definely take the walk all the way down to the south end of the beach. It generally gets rockier as you go and your odds of finding nice agates will improve.

Go past the lighthouse and walk south for rockier beaches.

22. North Beach County Park

Directions:

From downtown Port Townsend, take Tyler Street north for a few blocks and then veer left on F Street. Continue on F Street for about 0.75 miles, then turn right on San Juan Ave. Continue north for about 1 mile and the road will turn left, turning into 49th Street. In about 0.2 miles, turn left on Kuhn Street and follow it north all the way to the parking lot.

Field Notes:

North Beach sits adjacent to Fort Warden Historical Park. This is a county park and requires no parking fee. This is a popular area with the locals, and has a nice network of trails in addition to beachcombing.

This is one of the most fun beaches to explore in this entire guide. There are plenty of agates to find here, but they are more of a bonus at this site. That's because lovely pieces of polished sea glass are very abundant at this beach, remnants from historic dumping that took place many decades ago. From the parking area, walking west toward McCurdy Point (also called Glass Beach) is good, or you can go east to Fort Warden Park. Either way, the pickin' was good. One word of caution here... pay special attention to the tides. The beach gets very "skinny" at high tide. All the glass in the pictures below were found in less than an hour.

All this sea glass was found in less than an hour at North Beach.

Pacific Coast & Strait of Juan de Fuca (Site Map)

23. Ediz Hook

Directions:

From Port Angeles, head west through town on Front Street. As you are leaving the downtown section, the road veers to the left and turns into Marine Drive. Follow it for approximately 3 miles and it will take you right out to the spit. There are several parking areas along the road, with the largest being at Harborview Park.

Field Notes:

Ediz Hook is a 3-mile long sand spit. It has been reenforced with large rocks and sees a fair number of visitors. The Coast Guard is situated at the end of the spit, limiting public access to the last mile of Ediz Hook.

I had high hopes for Ediz Hook as an agate hunting site, but I have yet to find a nice agate there. I'm sure they do show up from time to time, but I haven't ever had much luck. I have found a few pieces of orbicular jasper which are really neat. Its close proximitely to Port Angeles and the historic dumping that took place does mean that sea glass is present here. However, unlike at North Beach, 99% of the pieces I find here are more modern trash. The nice frosty, polished sea glass takes some effort to find. The big blue piece in the picture was the only polished piece I found on my last visit.

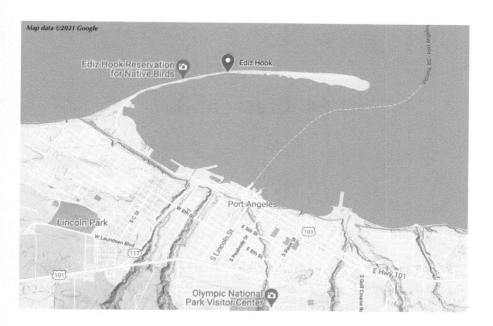

A big trophy sea glass like this makes the trip worth it!

24. Crescent Bay

Directions:

From Port Angeles, head west on Highway 101 for about 5 miles, the turn on the Strait of Juan de Fuca Highway. Continue for about 6.2 miles, then turn right on Camp Hayden Road and continue north for about 4 miles. This public access is adjacent to the Salt Creek Recreation Area, but you will drive past the main entrance to Tounge Point Park and park in the lot just before the bridge over Salt Creek.

Field Notes:

This is a beautiful beach popular with surfers. The campground at Tounge Point Park is definitely worth staying at if you decide to spend a few days here. However, the shoreline at the campground is rocky, with tide pools and difficult access. For agate hunting, you will want to go to Crescent Bay.

The public parking site is a Clallam County park, so there is no fee. However, most of Crescent Bay is actually private land. You can only access the beach on the east side of Salt River. Everything west of the river is private and posted. You can pay an access fee if you want to, but there is a decent section of beach that you can explore without paying for access. There are usually some nice "pea gravels" that have small agates and other good material to explore.

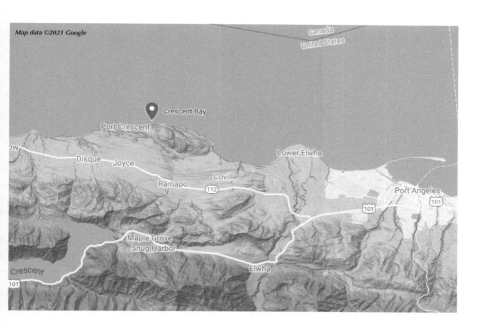

25. Murdock Beach

Directions:

From Port Angeles, head west on Highway 101 for about 5 miles, the turn on the Strait of Juan de Fuca Highway. Head west for about 16 miles and you'll see a sign for Murdock Beach access. Turn right and follow the road toward the beach. There is a split in the road that is not well marked, but turn right at the split and you will quickly arrive at the parking area.

Field Notes:

Discover Pass required. Bathroom facility on site. There is a very short hike from the parking lot down to the beach. The trail comes out close to the mouth of Murdock Creek. This site is best visited during a negative or low tide. Otherwise the beach is quite narrow without much to explore. Time it right and you will have lots of rocky shoreline to explore. The variety of rocks is great at Murdock Beach, with plenty of nice material to bring home and tumble.

You can find good jaspers (including orbicular jaspers) and plenty of agates at this site. This is also a good beach to keep your eyes peeled for marine fossils, often appearing as fragments or within sandstone concretions.

If you are camping, check out the Lyre River Campground just east of here.

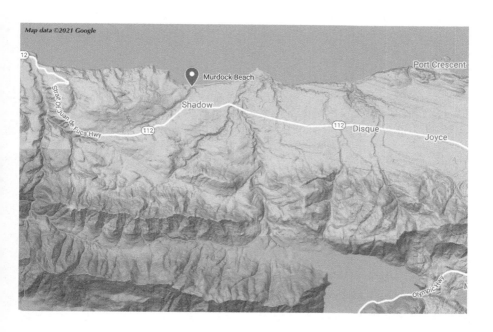

The short path down to Murdock Beach.

26. Twin River Beach

Directions:

From Port Angeles, head west on Highway 101 for about 5 miles, the turn on the Strait of Juan de Fuca Highway. Continue west for 22 miles. The highway drops down and as soon as you see the water, look for a dirt road that drops down to the parking area.

Field Notes:

This is a Clallam County access. No parking fee. No services, aside from 2 porta potties that were on site when I visited. It looks like the area east of the parking lot is posted private, but the area between the parking lot and the mouth of the West Twin River provides enough gravel to keep you busy for days. I found the big clear/smoky agate on my last visit here and also picked some nice green and red jaspers.

There is another access if you continue west on the main highway and park at the wide turnout just as you cross the bridge. It's a bit more challenging to scramble down to the water, but there's even more shoreline for you to explore on this side of the West Twin River. Be cautious of the large waves at this site, as the shore can be steep and the waves larger as we are getting closer to the Pacific Ocean. Never turn your back on big waves, and keep an eye on children.

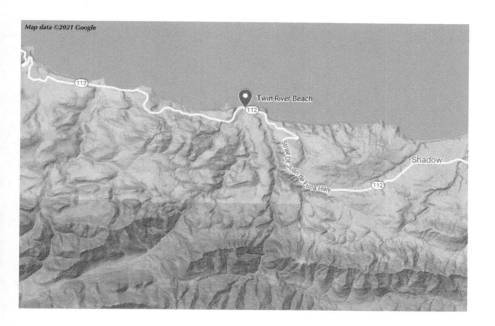

You could spend days and days exploring the gravel at the mouth of Twin River.

27. Clallam Bay "West"

Directions:

From the big turn in the highway in downtown Clallam Bay, continue west for another 0.5 miles. Look for the sign for the park. Note that it is a sharp turn to get down to the parking area, and it might be best to go up the highway and turn around so you are approaching the parking lot from west to east.

Field Notes:

Clallam County park. No parking fee. There is also a state park access to the beach right in town, but on my last visit the walking bridge that crosses over Clallam River was washed out and I couldn't find a way to access the beach without swimming. Not only does the Clallam Bay "West" site provide easy access, but you can also avoid the need for a Discover Pass.

This is a fantastic rockhounding site with over 1 mile of public beach access to Clallam Bay. This is a fun site with lots of variety. Agates, jaspers, sea glass, shells and ancient marine fossils... just about everything that the beach offers can be found here. You've got a full mile of beach to explore and rocks covering most of it. Lots of variety and plenty of different colored rocks to bring home for the rock tumbler.

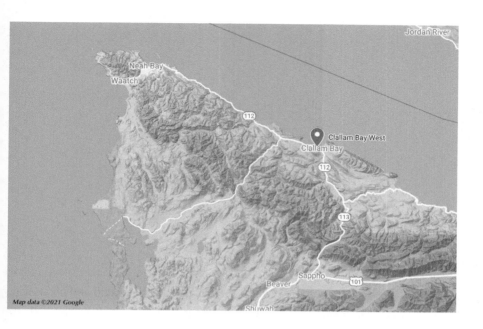

Talk about variety! Shells, starfish, sea glass, jaspers and agates.

28. Rialto Beach

Directions:

From Forks, head north on Highway 101 for 1.5 miles. Turn left on La Push Road and continue west for 7.8 miles. Turn right on Mora Road and go another 5 miles to the parking area for Rialto Beach. From the parking area, head north and you will be on National Park Service land. Walk south toward the Quillayute River and you will be on tribal land.

Field Notes:

Rialto Beach is partly tribal lands and partly National Park Service land. You'll need to get a vehicle pass for the Olympic National Park to park in the lot, which at the time of this writing costs you $30 for a 1 week pass.

Tribal lands also cover a rocky section at the mouth of the Quillayute River. This is probably the most famous beach in Washington, with jagged basalt spires sticking up out of the Pacific Ocean. Please read the _"Regulations: Rockhounding on Washington Beaches"_ section at the beginning of this book and make your choices. I know old rockhounds who have been picking up rocks here for decades and never had any problems, but it's your choice.

This beach is loaded with orbicular jaspers. Their fascinating "orb" patterns are quite unique and make them a real treasure.

Orbicular "poppy" jaspers at Rialto Beach.

29. First Beach

Directions:

From Forks, head north on Highway 101 for 1.5 miles. Turn on La Push Road and go about 14 miles, all the way to La Push.

Field Notes:

This beach is located on the Quileute Indian Reservation. I've never heard of any issues with collecting rocks on tribal lands.

There are no bad days at this beach... this is one of the most beautiful places in the Pacific Northwest. A popular site with surfers and beachcombers alike.

Orbicular jaspers are abundant here. Look for these dark red stones scattered amongst the basalt stones on the beach. You can find them year-round, but the best collecting will be in the winter months when storms push fresh material up on the beaches.

If you visit during the winter, the jasper hunting can be amazing. There is a good chance that you will find enough jaspers to fill a bucket, but I would encourage you to high grade as you go, and only collect a modest amount. Bring home a pocketful of select pieces and leave a few for other rockhounds to enjoy.

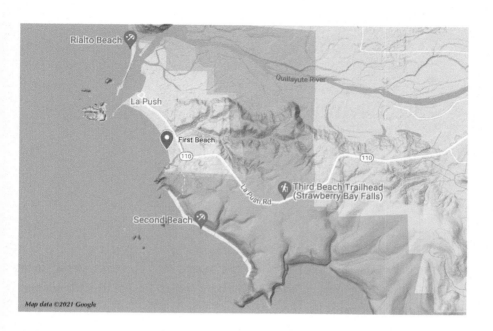

A nice handful of jaspers found at First Beach near La Push.

30. Olympic National Park Beaches

Directions:

The beaches of the Olympic National Park cover over 73 miles, covering most of the Pacific Coast starting from the Makah Indian Reservation down near the mouth of the Queets River on the Quinault Indian Reservation. There are a small sections of shoreline owned by the Ozette, Quileute, and Hoh Indians, but most of the Pacific Coast on the Olympic Peninsula is part of the ONP.

Field Notes:

There are many great agate hunting beaches within the Olympic National Park. If you like to go "by the book," then the rock collecting regulations are quite clear. From the NPS:

"Collecting, rockhounding, and gold panning of rocks, minerals, and paleontological specimens, for either recreational or educational purposes is generally prohibited in all units of the National Park System (36 C.F.R. § 2.1(a) and § 2.5(a)). Violators of this prohibition are subject to criminal penalties."

Unofficially, I spoke to a park ranger while I was scouting locations for this guide book, and the feeling that I got was that beachcombing wasn't a very big concern. Making sure visitors have paid their $30 access fees seems to be the top priority. Regarding picking up rocks on the beach, the one I spoke with told me, and I quote, "we're really not too concerned with that." Of course, he was talking about *casual use collecting*. Digging, destructive activity, or collecting more than a few pocket rocks is going to bring you problems.

Please read the *"Regulations: Rockhounding on Washington Beaches"* section at the beginning of this book and make your choices. I know rockhounds who have been picking up rocks here for decades and never had any problems, but it's your choice. For the purposes of this book, I am only telling you where you can *FIND* agates. Whether you decide to put them in your pocket is your decision. A few of the beaches you might want to check out include:

· Shi Shi Beach (4 mile roundtrip hike)
· 2nd Beach (2.1 mile roundtrip hike)
· 3rd Beach (2.8 mile roundtrip hike)
· Ruby Beach (<0.2 miles from parking lot down to the beach)
· Kolaloch Beach 4 (0.8 mile roundtrip hike)

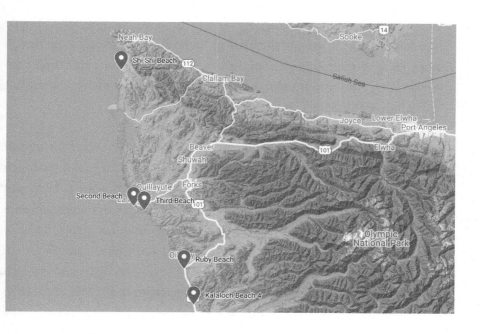

31. Roosevelt Beach

Directions:

From Ocean Shores, head north on Highway 115. Turn left on Highway 109 and head north for 10 miles. Turn left on Roosevelt Beach Road and take it all the way to the beach. You are allowed to drive on the beach at this access.

Field Notes:

This is a sandy beach most of the year. Successful rockhounding will be highly dependent on storms moving the sand and exposing gravels. My main reason for including this site is because of the accessibility. You can drive right onto the beach here, so someone with mobility issues could literally rockhound out of the window of their car if they wanted to!

Head south on the beach for about a mile and you will be at Iron Spring and the mouth of Boone Creek. This area would be worth checking out if the beach is all sanded up. There can be some nice big jaspers in this area. There are several accesses both north and south of here that are very similar. Some are county accesses that let you drive on the beach, others are state parks that have camping available. Mocrocks Beach in Moclips, Pacific Beach and Seabrook Beach all provide access. Rockhounding will likely be similar, and if beach conditions are right there will be agates and jaspers to find. Most of the time expect wide sandy beaches that are more suited for sand dollars and seashells.

You can drive your car on Roosevelt Beach. Don't get stuck!

32. Damon Point

Directions:

From the main traffic circle as you enter Ocean Shores, continue south on Point Brown Avenue NE for 4.5 miles. Turn right on Discovery Avenue SE and look for the main parking area in about 0.2 miles, immediately after the RV Park. There is a large welcome sign that also provides some information about closed areas during critical nesting times and other site rules.

Field Notes:

Free Parking. This is one of the top agate hunting sites in Washington, and probably the best place to fill your pockets on a consistent basis. Damon Point extends for 2.25 miles from the parking area out to the tip of the sand spit on the north side of Grays Harbor. Brilliant orange/red carnelian agates are the prize at Damon Point. On a good day you can find lots of them, along with just about everything else. The gravel beds can be colorful and exciting to search through. Orbicular jaspers are also common here.

The most productive area for rockhounds is consistently out on the far end of the point. If you are up for the hike, then plan on spending several hours. There are porta-potties at the parking area, but there are no facilities out on the point. If you're not up for the 4.5 mile roundtrip hike that's okay too. You can usually still find some good material closer to the parking lot as well.

Damon Point is probably the most reliable site to find big carnelian agates.

33. Westhaven State Park

Directions:

From Westport, go north on N. Montesano St. for about 1 mile. Turn left on Jetty Haul Road and go another mile to arrive at the parking lot.

Field Notes:

Discover Pass required. There are a couple different beach accesses from Westport to Cohassett Beach, but I have found the best gravels to be concentrated close to the Westport Jetty. The closer to the mouth of the Grays Harbor the better.

You will find good gravel beds that hide nice agates. This isn't as reliable a producer as Damon Point, and if the driving distance is similar I would probably go to Damon Point, but this site is still worth visiting. Most beaches south of here down to the mouth of the Columbia are predominantly sand, so this is one of the southernmost beaches were you can still expect to find good agates and jaspers. There's also no shortage of sand dollars.

Sand dollars are more abundant than agates, but you'll find both if you time it right.

Rock Tumbling

Throughout this book you've heard me reference the good "tumbler material" that you can find all across the Washington shoreline. Every serious Washington beachcomber should have a rock tumbler. Tumbling is an inexpensive hobby, and **it's a great way to bring the fun back with you when you get home from the beach!**

Rock tumbling is an easy and fun hobby. It's a great way to polish up the colorful beach stones that you find along the Washington Coast.

Equipment

Most importantly, you will need a **rotary rock tumbler**. These range in size and quality. Inexpensive ones can be found for as little as $40. They do work, but they are constructed with plastic components and will not last long. If you only intend to use it a few times then one of the cheap ones will probably be fine, but I would encourage you to get one slightly better.

Harbor Freight Tools sells a few different tumblers that I have heard good things about. They are more in the $50 to $70 range, but they will hold up better than the cheap plastic ones. Other mid-grade tumblers from various brands can be found in this price range.

My tumbler is a Lortone Model 33B. It has two barrels allowing you to tumble two different batches at the same time. Lortone tumblers cost in the $100 to $200 range, but they are durable and will last for decades if you treat them right.

The second item that you will need is **abrasive media** or **grit**. To complete the full cycle, you will need coarse, medium, pre-polish and final polish compounds. They can be purchased inexpensively from your local rock shop and many online retailers.

The third must have item is a **colander** or **sieve**. This will be used to rinse the grit off your rocks at the end of each polishing cycle. Nothing fancy here. You can probably get one at your local dollar store.

Selecting the Best Stones

First we need to select our stones. To take a polish, a stone needs to be **hard**. Soft, porous stones will not hold up to the tumbling process and won't achieve the desired results.

Agates and jasper will take a polish, and many other stones that you can find on Washington beaches will also polish up nicely.

Finding out which stones will polish the best can often take some trial and error. That's part of the fun of rock tumbling. Sometimes the more "boring" looking rocks will come out of the tumbler and look amazing. I've found the best rocks to tumble are the ones that look beautiful when wet, but get dull and boring once they have dried out. The tumbling process can really bring out the beauty of these stones.

Smooth stones are usually best. Rocks that have fractures or jagged texture will need more time in the tumbler to achieve the desired result.

Loading the Barrel

Tumbling is a fun, easy process. Basically all that we are doing is taking our raw stones and running them through various cycles of polishing, where we use finer and finer textured tumbling compounds.

Once we have selected the stones that we want to tumble, we need to load them into the barrel. Easy enough – just unscrew the top and load it about 2/3 full with stones. Rinse the stones off first so they are clean from any sand or dirt. Don't overfill the barrel. A void is required to allow the stones to roll inside and tumble properly.

Ideally, the stones should be comparable in size. A range from 1/4" to 1" diameter stones would be a good first run. The grit in the tumbler is moved by the rocks, so any large discrepencies in size can prevent ideal coverage of the grit. Try to keep rocks of similar size in each load.

The Tumbling Process

This is a 4-step process that will take the better part of a month to complete. First we begin with a coarse grit, then move on to the medium, then pre-polish, and then the final polish. Often the grits you buy will simply be labeled Step 1, 2, 3, and 4.

The most important thing is that you do them in the right order, as each stage of the process will use a finer and finer grit. After the final stage, you should be left with bright, shiny stones.

I am adding coarse grit for the first stage of the tumbling process.

Step 1: Coarse Grit - Grinding & Shaping

In Step 1, fill your barrel 2/3 full with various beach stones. No need to separate by type. Agates, jaspers and various colored rocks can be added together as long as they are similar in size. Add the coarse grit to the barrel. The proper amount will depend on the size of your tumbler and quantity of the rocks. When you buy grit it should include instructions on how much to add.

Fill the barrel with just enough water so that the top of the rocks still stick out of the water. Don't overfill with water or the tumbling process will not work properly. Put the lid on the barrel and put it on the tumbler.

Plug in the tumbler and let it run for a day. After 24 hours, open the barrel and inspect the stones. Although fairly uncommon, some materials can cause gas buildup and should be vented occasionally to prevent excess pressure in the barrel. Reseal and continue tumbling with the coarse grit for 7 more days.

After the cycle is completed, the stones need to be rinsed of all grit and any trace of abrasive. To clean the stones of all grit, pour everything into your **colander** and thoroughly rinse the stones. A word of caution: **DO NOT RINSE THE GRIT DOWN THE SINK. It will cause all sorts of problems with your plumbing system.** Rinse the grit off into a bucket or some other container where it can be collected and disposed of properly. Don't forget to rinse out the inside of the barrel in preparation for the next step.

Step 2: Medium Grit - Smoothing

Put the freshly rinsed stones back into the barrel. Add the proper amount of medium grit and seal up the barrel. Put it back on the tumbler and let it roll for 7 more days. After a week, open it up and inspect a few stones. There should be a smooth, matte surface across all the stones. If needed, feel free to continue tumbling for 2 or 3 more days. When finished, rinse off the stones as detailed in Step 1.

Step 3: Pre-Polish

Before starting Step 3, take a close look at all your stones and make sure they are all smooth with no cracks or sharp edges. Any sharp edges at this point will harm the final polishing process, so remove any rocks that aren't nice and smooth.

Add the proper amount of pre-polish and water, again adding just enough water that the top stones just peek out. Seal up the barrel and let it run for another 7-10 days. If in doubt, its best to err on the long side. A few extra days won't hurt anything, but not giving the tumblers enough time to finish the cycle will result in an unsatisfactory final result. Rinse off the stones as detailed in Step 1.

Thoroughly rinse your rocks after each step of the tumbling process.

Step 4: Final Polish

This stage requires extra care to ensure that you get the perfect final polish. Make extra sure that your stones have all been carefully rinsed, as well as the empty barrel. Any contamination will result in less than perfect results. Put the stones back in the barrel, add the proper amount of polish, and tumble for 7 days.

After the full week has passed, rinse each stone as best as you can.

Step 5: Burnishing (Optional)

When you take your finished stones out of the final polish you might find that it's difficult to rinse off all the extra-fine polishing compounds. This is especially common with stones that still have small grooves, cracks or fissures. The white residue left behind can be tough to completely remove. Burnishing will help.

This final step is not absolutely necessary, but it is often helpful to get your stones fully cleaned off. This step should take less than an hour, and will ensure that your polished stones end up clean and shiny.

Rinse the final polish off of your stones as best you can. Rinse out the barrel of your tumbler as well. Put your polished stones back in, and fill with just enough warm water to cover all the stones.

Next, add some soap to the drum. Some people use powdered laundry detergent, but I simply take a bar of soap and shave off some pieces into the drum with the rocks. About 1 tablespoon of soap shaving in a drum of 2-3 pounds of stones is about right.

Seal everything up and let it tumble for an hour or so. No need to leave it much longer than that. The warm soapy water will help to clean up the stones and remove any fine polish that was still clinging to the stones after the final rinse.

After an hour, pull out your stones and rinse everything off. If the entire tumbling process was followed carefully, you should be greeted with some lovely polished rocks!

Made in the USA
Las Vegas, NV
18 May 2023

72239752R00066